THE SNOW QUEEN

HANS CHRISTIAN ANDERSEN

Once, long ago, there was a girl named Gerda and a boy named Kai. They lived next door to each other and were the best of friends. Between their two houses was a garden where Gerda and Kai played among the flowers all summer long. Of all the flowers that bloomed there, the roses were Gerda's favorite.

When winter came, Gerda and Kai sat by the warm stove and listened to Kai's grandmother tell stories about the wicked Snow Queen.

"Her heart is a block of ice," Grandmother warned. "And she would like to make everyone's heart as cold and icy as her own."

As the old woman spoke, the wind howled outside. A window flew open and a splinter of ice blew into Kai's eye. The icicle traveled instantly to his heart and stayed there.

After that day Kai changed into a rude and cruel boy. Though he often hurt her feelings, Gerda did not know that it was the splinter of ice that was freezing his heart.

The boys liked to tie their sleds to the farmer's cart and let it pull them across the snow. One day, Kai saw a big white sleigh in the square. The driver was dressed in white fur.

"This will be more exciting," he thought, and he hitched his sled to the white sleigh.

The sleigh moved off — faster and faster — until Kai began to get frightened. They flew with the wind for hours. At last they stopped and the driver stood up. Kai stared in wonder. There before him stood the Snow Queen. She bent and kissed his forehead. Her touch froze his heart completely and he forgot all about Gerda and his grandmother.

Gerda waited all winter for Kai to come home.

In the springtime, she put on her new red shoes and went down to the river. "Have you seen my friend Kai?" she asked the waves. "If you tell me where he is I'll give you my new shoes."

It seemed to Gerda that the waves were nodding to her. She climbed into a little boat, and as she tossed her shoes into the water the boat drifted from the bank and raced downstream. Though she was frightened she thought, "Perhaps the boat will take me to Kai."

The boat carried Gerda down the river until it passed a little house beside a cherry orchard. A strange old woman came out of the cottage. She hooked the boat with her crooked walking stick and pulled it to the shore.

"Poor child," she said to Gerda. "How did you come to be floating all alone through the wide world?"

Gerda told the old woman her story, and asked if she had seen Kai.

"He's not been here yet, my dear, but I expect he will be very soon."

The old woman took Gerda into the house and gave her some cherries to eat. While Gerda ate, the old woman combed her hair.

Now in truth, the old woman was the loneliest of all magicians, and she wanted to keep Gerda with her. So, using her magic, she combed away all her memories. Soon Gerda forgot about Kai.

For days, Gerda played in the cottage. But one morning she saw a bush blooming with red roses in the garden. Right away she remembered Kai. "I've stayed here too long!" she cried.

A big black crow heard her and asked what was wrong.

"I have to find my friend Kai. Have you seen him?"

"I saw a boy pass this way. He married a Princess and now they live in a palace nearby," said the crow.

"Can you show me the way there?" asked Gerda.

The crow flew off and led Gerda to the palace.

Gerda crept upstairs to the royal bedroom. She peeped in at the sleeping Prince and burst into tears. "It isn't Kai," she sobbed.

Her crying woke the Prince and Princess. They listened quietly to her story, and then the Princess said, "Take this pretty dress to wear."

"I'll give you my golden coach," said the Prince, "so you can travel farther and faster and find Kai."

Gerda rode swiftly through the forest. Some wicked thieves saw the gleaming coach and cried, "It's gold! All gold!" They captured Gerda and took her to their hideaway. But when they discovered that she wasn't a rich Princess, Gerda was in great danger.

"Don't harm her," pleaded the boss thief's daughter. "She can play with me."

Her father scowled. "All right," he grumbled, "but lock her up and see that she doesn't escape."

That night Gerda told her friend about Kai, and how she longed to find him. The doves in the rafters and an old reindeer listened to her story.

One of the doves started to coo very loudly, "We've seen Kai. He was riding with the Snow Queen as she flew toward Lapland."

"I must go there," cried Gerda.

The thief's daughter took the key from her sleeping father. Then she said to the reindeer, "Lapland is your home. Take Gerda there quickly and help her to find Kai."